Curious Facts 2

Curious Facts 2

JOHN MAY

SECKER & WARBURG
LONDON

First published in England 1984 by
Martin Secker & Warburg Ltd
54 Poland Street, London W1V 3DF

Copyright © by John May

ISBN 0–436–27442–6

Printed and bound in Great Britain by
Butler & Tanner Ltd., Frome

ACKNOWLEDGEMENT

This book is dedicated to Tanya Seton, who would like it to be publicly stated that if it hadn't been for her none of this could have happened. She's right about most things. She has been through it all. What a hero.

I NTRODUCTION

This is a book about the random nature of real life, the relativity of experience, the pursuit of knowledge, the compression of information and the nature of truth. It is also a book about menstruating men, the evolution of the pencil, Japanese paper folding, accident-prone people, hamburgers, underground buildings, fire eaters, protein decay and Oman. It exists outside the confines of traditional scholarship and enquiry, a refuge for pieces of fugitive information, a place where they can breathe easy and not have to worry about their inability to fit into existing categories. This is a book dedicated to diversity and the disruption of set modes of thinking, an organic encyclopedia of anomalies for an age when new patterns of thought are emerging from the biological mix.

In *Eccentric Spaces*, an unusual work in its own right, Robert Harbinson comments: 'Though it occasionally seems a place for things that belong nowhere, for a lot of homeless information, a catalogue is also an attempt to begin over again with the atoms of knowledge . . . a catalogue always loses the mind in a fertile chaos of jostling characters.' This book is a catalogue of sorts, a Sears and Roebuck of the imagination for those in need of Brain Tonic, Expanding Hair Lacquer, Oxygen Cocktails and a Coincidence Mirror for the hallway.

It could also be considered a piece of conceptual art – a holographic information matrix, a glistening patchwork of diatoms – or a piece of illusionist's equipment.

Like *The Circus of Dr Lao* this is also a travelling show, a developing entertainment, a live performance. Roll up and see